When I Eat

First published in 1991 by Firefly Books Limited.

This edition published in 1993 by Wayland (Publishers) Ltd.

This revised edition published in 2009 by Wayland,
338 Euston Road, London NW1 3BH.

Wayland Australia
Level 17/207 Kent Street, Sydney, NSW 2000

Consultant: Jane Battell

British Library Cataloguing in Publication Data
Suhr, Mandy
When I eat.–(I'm alive)
1. Food–Pictorial works–Juvenile literature.
2. Nutrition–Pictorial works–Juvenile literature.
3. Digestion–Pictorial works–Juvenile literature.
I. Title II. Series III. Gordon, Mike.
612.3-3dc22

ISBN 9780750259491

Printed in China

Wayland is a division of Hachette Children's Books,
an Hachette UK company.

www.hachette.co.uk

I'm Alive!

When I Eat

Written by Mandy Suhr
Illustrated by Mike Gordon

WAYLAND

When I was a tiny baby I had no teeth. I couldn't chew but I could suck, so I drank lots of milk.

Milk is very good for many babies.

As I grew older, I could eat soft, squashy food and special baby food.

Then my teeth started to grow.

Soon I had strong teeth and
I could eat all sorts of food.
I need food to give my body
energy to move and to grow.

When I put food into my mouth, I chew it up and swallow it. Then the food begins its journey through my body.

Along the way my body breaks
the food up and sorts it into
the parts I need and waste.

RUMBLE
RUMBLE

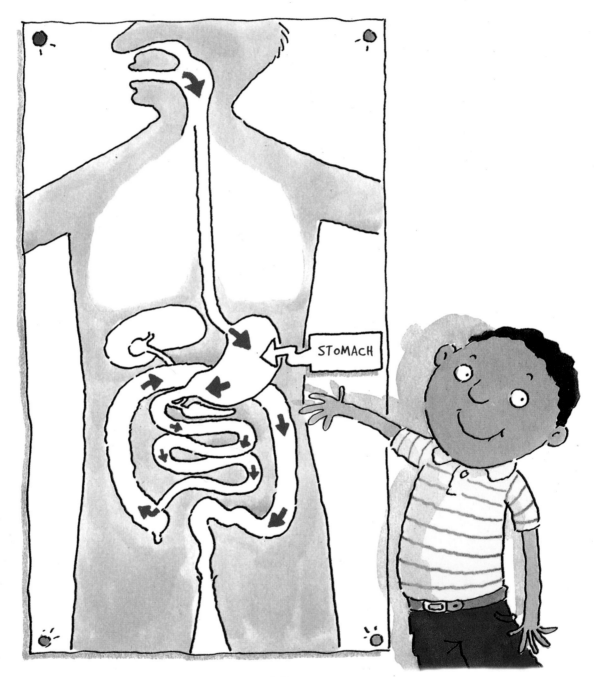

STOMACH

The food is pushed down a long tube into my stomach. Here it gets mixed even more and goes into another tube.

This tube takes out the parts of the food that I need and puts them into my blood.

My blood takes these useful parts around my body to where they are needed.

My body doesn't need
the waste food, so it goes
along more tubes to my...

14

...bottom.

When I go to the toilet the
waste food comes out.

I feed my pets special food.
But animals in the wild find
their own food.

Some animals eat plants
and leaves. Some catch
other animals to eat.

Plants make their
own food in
their leaves.

They also suck in special
parts of the soil through their
roots to help them to grow.

Some foods are really good for us. This is because they are full of the things that our bodies need to work properly.

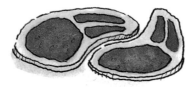

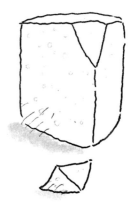

Milk and cheese, meat, fish and beans have proteins that help us to grow.

Fruit and vegetables have vitamins and minerals that help us to stay healthy.

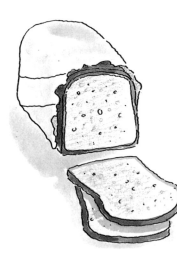

Bread, potatoes and pasta give us energy.

21

To grow strong and healthy we should eat lots of these good foods. We also need lots of exercise and fresh air.

Why do you think these meals would be good for you?

23

Notes for Adults

I'm Alive is a series of first information books particularly suitable for the early and emergent stages of reading.

Each book in the series includes simple, factual text, and amusing and colourful illustrations, to combine reading for pleasure with fact-finding.

The series takes a closer look at the human body and how it works and develops, comparing this with other forms of life. **I'm Alive** is designed to address the requirements of the National Curriculum for Science at key stage 1.

The books are equally suitable for use at school or at home.
Below are some suggestions for extension activities that can be carried out with children to complement and extend the learning in this book.

Extension Activities

1 To be healthy, we need to eat a mixture of foods. Record what you eat in day. Sort this into different food groups.

2 Do you think you have a healthy diet? What are your favourite foods? Choose one of these and make a poster to advertise it.

3 Lots of food are made from a mixture of other foods. Collect food packets and investigate what these foods are made from.

4 Make play food from plasticine. Put it on a paper plate. Make a healthy meal and one which is not so healthy. How are they different?